C000186676

Firsts and ~~Seconds~~

AN INTRODUCTION
TO TWO-PART SINGING

William Appleby
and
Frederick Fowler

OXFORD UNIVERSITY PRESS
MUSIC DEPARTMENT GREAT CLARENDON STREET OXFORD OX2 6DP

795

FOREWORD

THIS collection is designed to be an introduction to two-part singing. There is nothing unusual in the use of rounds and canons for this purpose : what is unusual is that here they are written out in full. Too often each part is sung with a fine disregard for the other : here it is hoped that the eye will help the ear not only in its own part but in that of its partner also. The rounds and canons have been carefully graded and, in general, are not widely known.

Following the rounds and canons are simple arrangements in which the second part is vocalised. The singers thus become accustomed to holding an independent part against a melody and, once again, the grading is such that the transition to a really interesting and independent part should be easy.

Finally, we give two-part songs of varying periods. Nos. 16 and 17 were originally glees for two upper voices and bass. We have made certain modifications, again in the interests of simplicity.

The music of the following numbers has been arranged by the editors : 1 to 6, 8, 9, 14, 15, 16, 17.

W. A. and F. F.

LIST OF SONGS

1. Tallis's Canon
2. The Cuckoo *(traditional)*
3. All who sing, and wish to please *(T. Goodban)*
4. The hart he loves the high wood *(traditional)*
5. Now we are met *(T. Goodban)*
6. Haste thee, nymph *(Samuel Arnold)*
7. The Sandman *(German folk-tune, arr. Brahms)*
8. Blow the wind southerly *(Northumbrian folksong)*
9. The Miller's Flowers *(Schubert)*
10. Susanni *(Old German tune, arr. Fritz Jöde)*
11. The Shepherd *(Harry Brook)*
12. Song of the Spirits (from 'Armide') *(Gluck)*
13. O wha's for Scotland, and Charlie?
    (Jacobite song, arr. Herbert Horrocks)
14. Sweet Kate *(Robert Jones)*
15. Summer (from 'Alcina') *(Handel)*
16. How merrily we live *(Michael Este)*
17. The Loadstars *(William Shield)*
18. Ho-la-hi *(German folksong, arr. Roger Fiske)*
19. Song of Farewell *(Austrian folksong, arr. Ferdinand Rauter)*
20. Li'l David, play on yo' harp
    (Negro spiritual, arr. Sebastian H. Brown)
21. Cielito Lindo *(Mexican folk-tune, arr. Phyllis Tate)*

FIRSTS AND SECONDS

1. Tallis's Canon

Words by
Bishop Ken (1637-1711)

Thomas Tallis
(c. 1505-1585)

First Voice: Glo-ry to thee, my God, this night For

Second Voice: Glo-ry to thee, my God, this night For

all the bless-ings of the light; Keep me, O keep me, King of kings, Be-

all the bless-ings of the light; Keep me, O keep me, King of kings, Be-

-neath thy own al - migh - ty wings. Praise God, from whom all

-neath thy own al - migh - ty wings. Praise

bless - ings flow; Praise him, all crea - tures here be - low; Praise him a - bove, ye

God, from whom all bless - ings flow; Praise him, all crea - tures here be - low; Praise

heav'n - ly host; Praise Fa - ther, Son, and Ho - ly Ghost. A - men.

him a - bove, ye heav'n - ly host; Praise Fa - ther, Son, and Ho - ly Ghost. A - men.

Firsts and Seconds

2. The Cuckoo

Words by
Jacqueline Froom

Traditional

From far a - way it ech - oes, His clear and joy - ful song: It rings a - cross the val - ley In spring the whole day long. "Cuc - koo, cuc - koo," he sings with might and

From far a - way it ech - oes, His clear and joy - ful

6

3. All who sing, and wish to please

T. Goodban
(1784-1863)

4. The hart he loves the high wood

Traditional

First Voice: The hart he loves the high wood, The
hare she loves the hill; The knight he loves his bright sword, The
girls they like their will, The girls they like their will.

Second Voice: The
hart he loves the high wood, The hare she loves the hill; The
knight he loves his bright sword, The girls they like their will.

5. Now we are met

T. Goodban
(1784-1863)

6. Haste thee, nymph

Words by
John Milton

Samuel Arnold
(1740-1802)

*originally

Firsts and Seconds

7. The Sandman

Words by
Frances B. Wood

German folk-tune
arranged by Brahms

Note: the second voice part has been added by the editors. The words are reprinted by permission.

gown of sil - ver dressed.
flowers and child - ren too.

"Gone is Day, Time" they say, "For the
"Lit - tle ones, Pret - ty, ones Now

lah   lah   lah lah lah   lah   lah lah   lah

bu - sy world to rest."
sleep the long night through."

lah lah   lah   lah

2. They

2. Lah

14

8. Blow the wind southerly

Northumbrian folk-song

9. The Miller's Flowers

Translated by
Arthur Langford

Franz Schubert
(1797-1828)

The words are reprinted by permission

murm - 'ring stream Whose wa - ters in___ the sun - light gleam.
daugh - ter fair Leans out___ to breathe the sum - mer air,
sleep___ she lies, They'll nev - er close___ their own___ blue eyes,

lah   lah   lah   lah   lah

These   are___ my own___ for-get - me - nots,
Sure - ly___ she'll then___ for-get me not,
For   they___ are my___ for-get - me - nots.

lah   lah   lah   lah   lah___

These   are___ my own___ for-get - me - nots.
Sure - ly___ she'll then___ for-get me not.
For   they___ are my___ for-get - me - - nots.

lah   lah   lah___   lah___   lah.   lah.

1 & 2   D.S. vv. 2, 3   3

Firsts and Seconds

10. Susanni

Carol in two parts

15th-century words

Old German tune
arranged by Fritz Jöde

2. Now Jesus is the childès name,
   And Mary mild she is his dame;
   And so our sorrow is turned to game.

3. It fell upon the high midnight,
   The stars they shone both fair and bright,
   The angels sang with all their might.

4. Three kings there came with their presénts
   Of myrrh and gold and frankincense,
   As clerkès sing in their sequence.

5. Now sit we down upon our knee,
   And pray we to the Trinity,
   Our help, and succour for to be.

Words from *The Oxford Book of Carols*, by permission

11. The Shepherd

Words by
William Blake

Harry Brook

Firsts and Seconds

12. Song of the Spirits

from 'Armide'

Words by
Jacqueline Froom

Gluck (1714-1787)
Edited and arranged by
W. G. Whittaker

© 1930 (words) © 1964 Oxford University Press

CHORUS *(to be sung by both voices in both verses)*

Life! Thou must let us go! How - ev - er we re -

Life! Thou must let us go! How - ev - er we re -

\- gret, O free_ us from be - low: The world we_ must for -

\- gret, O free_ us from be - low: The world we must for -

\- get._ Hea - ven's gates o - pen_ wide And we must there a - bide._

\- get. Hea - ven's gates o - pen_ wide And we must there a - bide.

D.C. v. 2

13. Oh, wha's for Scotland and Charlie?

Traditional (Jacobite)
arranged by Herbert Horrocks

Tune from *Songs of Scotland* Vol. II (Boosey and Hawkes)

Firsts and Seconds

*Awa', auld carlie, = away old fellow.
**Whaur ye've been sae lang = where you've been so long.

Firsts and Seconds

14. Sweet Kate

Robert Jones (1609)

Moderato

First Voice / Second Voice / Piano

1. Sweet Kate of late Ran a-way and left me plain - ing. A - bide, I cried, Or I die with thy dis - dain - ing. Te he he, quoth she,
2. Un - kind, I find Thy de-light is in tor - ment - ing. A - bide, I cried, Or I die with thy con - sent - ing. Te he he, quoth she,

1. Sweet Kate of late Ran a - way and left me plain - ing. A - bide, I cried, Or I die with thy dis - dain - ing. Te he he, quoth she,
2. Un - kind, I find Thy de - light is in tor - ment - ing. A - bide, I cried, Or I die with thy con - sent - ing. Te he he, quoth she,

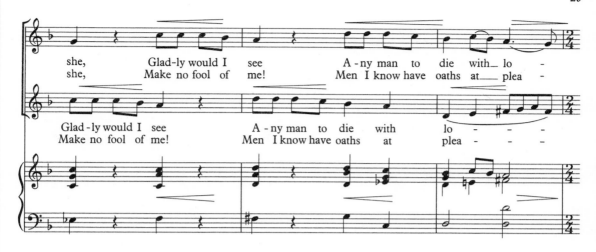

she,
Gladly would I see
Make no fool of me!

A-ny man to die with lo-
Men I know have oaths at plea-

Gladly would I see
Make no fool of me!

A-ny man to die with lo - - -
Men I know have oaths at plea - - -

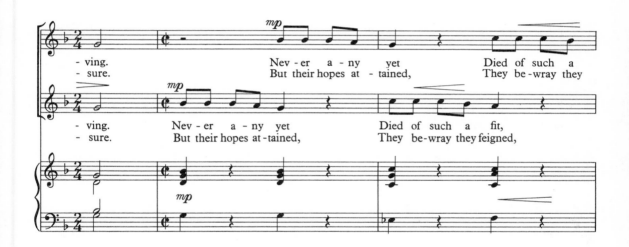

- ving.
- sure.

Nev-er a-ny yet
But their hopes at-tained,

Died of such a
They be-wray they

- ving.
- sure.

Nev - er a - ny yet
But their hopes at-tained,

Died of such a fit,
They be-wray they feigned,

fit,
feigned,

Nei-ther have I fear of pro - - ving.
And their oaths are kept at lei - - sure.

D.C. v. 2

Nei-ther have I fear of pro - - ving.
And their oaths are kept at lei - - sure.

D.C. v. 2

D.C. v. 2

★♮ last verse only

Firsts and Seconds

15. Summer

(Air from 'Alcina')

Words by
Jacqueline Froom

Handel
(1685-1759)

Firsts and Seconds

32

Firsts and Seconds

16. How merrily we live

Michael Este
(c. 1580-c. 1648)

the plea-sant downs, where as our flocks we see, We feel no

the plea-sant downs, where as our flocks we see, We feel no

cares, we fear not for - tune's frowns, We feel no

cares, we fear not, fear not for - tune's frowns, We feel no

cares, we fear not for - tune's frowns; We have no

cares, we fear not, fear not for - tune's frowns; We have no en - vy, we have no

en - vy, which sweet mirth, sweet mirth, sweet mirth con - founds, sweet

en - vy, which sweet mirth, sweet mirth, sweet mirth con - founds, sweet

mirth con - founds, con - founds,

mirth con - founds, We have no en - vy, which sweet mirth, sweet mirth con -

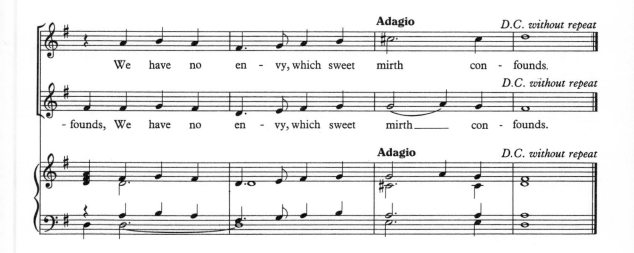

Adagio *D.C. without repeat*

We have no en - vy, which sweet mirth con - founds.

D.C. without repeat

- founds, We have no en - vy, which sweet mirth con - founds.

Adagio *D.C. without repeat*

Firsts and Seconds

17. The Loadstars

Words adapted
from Shakespeare

William Shield
(1748-1829)

40

42

Firsts and Seconds

18. Ho-la-hi

Translated by
Roger Fiske

German folk-song
arranged by Roger Fiske

ho - la - ho, That was not my dar - ling sweet, Ho - la - hi - a - ho.

First Voice *mf*
I - dle peo - ple

Second Voice *mf*
I - dle peo - ple

ques-tion me, Ho - la - hi, ho - la - ho, What my true love's name can be,

ques-tion me, Ho - la - hi, ho - la - ho, What my true love's name can be,

19. Song of farewell

Words by
Ursula Vaughan Williams

★ Austrian folk-song
Collected by Engel Lund
Arranged by Ferdinand Rauter

★From *A Second Book of Folk-songs* by Engel Lund (O.U.P.)

© Oxford University Press 1961

Firsts and Seconds

Firsts and Seconds

snow or rain. Friends I must for-get, think of me___ and say A

snow_ or_ rain. Friends I must for-get, O think of me and say A

pa - ter nos - ter at the end___ of day. A -

pa - ter nos - ter for me at the end of day.

-men, a - men, a - men. Your words will stand and keep Their

A - men, a - men. Your words will stand and

watch and guard a - round me___ where I sleep. A -

guard a - round me where I sleep. A -

- men,___ a - men. Your words will stand and keep Their

- men, a - men, a - men. Your words will stand and keep Their

watch and guard a - round me___ where I sleep.

watch and guard a - round me___ where___ I sleep.

Firsts and Seconds

20. Li'l David play on yo' harp

Negro Spiritual
arranged by Sebastian H. Brown

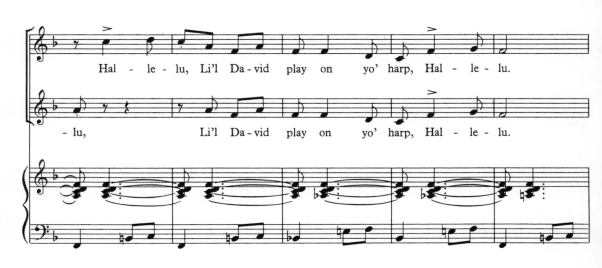

1. & 2. Li'l Da - vid play on yo' harp,

1. & 2. Li'l Da - vid play on yo' harp, Hal - le -

Hal - le - lu, Li'l Da - vid play on yo' harp, Hal - le - lu.

- lu, Li'l Da - vid play on yo' harp, Hal - le - lu.

Firsts and Seconds

Firsts and Seconds

Firsts and Seconds

21. Cielito Lindo

Words by
Jacqueline Froom

Mexican folk-tune
arranged by Phyllis Tate

* Pronounced "See*ay*-lee-to"

Firsts and Seconds

Firsts and Seconds

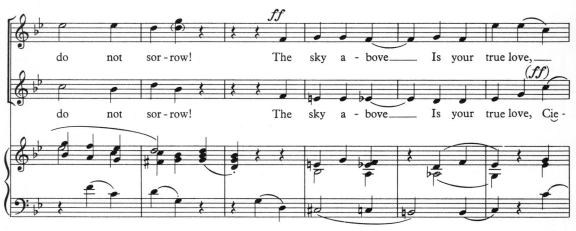

Firsts and Seconds

Processed and printed by
Halstan & Co. Ltd., Amersham, Bucks., England

OXFORD UNIVERSITY PRESS